Lifting Your Spirits
Seven Tools for Coping with Illness

CW00950955

When sickness comes, many people experience that
themselves". It is as though the body, sensing an er
thoughts and feelings towards itself, such that our normal human ability
to relate with kindness to others is reduced. Worry and irritability may
increase. Our spiritual reserves tend to be diminished.

Paradoxically, this process is the exact opposite of what the body really
needs to become well. Worry is not a healing feeling – it is the biggest
sickness in the world today. It drains us of strength.

Lifting Your Spirits is a wonderful guide because in it, Jan Alcoe shares
practical strategies aimed at countering worry and increasing well-being,
even in the face of serious illness.

The reason these strategies work is that they all address the "real me" as a
spiritual being, distinct from the body. When the inner being is properly
understood, the experience lifts the burden of worry.

It is as with the relationship between a driver and a car. Of course, the
car does need servicing from time to time. But if the driver does not take
proper care of herself or himself, and becomes filled with worry, anger, and
exhaustion, a serious accident becomes likely.

The quality of our thoughts, words and actions affects our health. If we
cause sorrow to others, that negativity will at some point rebound on us.
Conversely, when we act with kindness and compassion, the feelings of
goodwill that reach us from others help our health and healing. We get
blessings when we serve with love and sincerity.

I have had illness periodically throughout a long life, but I have always
taken it as an opportunity to strengthen my awareness of the inner being,
and deepen my relationship with God, the source of all goodness and
spiritual power. Seeing our honesty and courage, God helps us too.
This remembrance brings patience, and a deep peace that is healing for
the body, mind and spirit.

This experience creates trust in the benevolence of destiny, such that even
when the time comes, as it must, for me to leave this body, my final
moments will be good ones.

BK Janki

President, The Janki Foundation for Global Health Care

Lifting Your Spirits

Seven Tools for Coping with Illness

First Edition 2008
Second Edition 2009

The Janki Foundation for Global Health Care
449-451 High Road, London NW10 2JJ
United Kingdom
T +44 (0)20 8459 1400/9090
F +44 (0)20 8459 9091
E lys@jankifoundation.org
W www.jankifoundation.org

ISBN: 0-9548386-1-0

Cover and interior design: Jigsaw Design for Print
Butterfly illustrations: © Lou Beckerman www.loubeckerman.com
Printed in Italy by Mediaprint

Dedication

To Dadi Janki, President of The Janki Foundation for Global Health Care, for her inspiration and dedication to the improvement of patient care in the UK and worldwide.

Author: Jan Alcoe

Jan Alcoe is a hypnotherapist, writer and facilitator in health and social care, and publishing adviser to The Janki Foundation for Global Health Care. During her recent
treatment for cancer, she used the seven tools for her own sustenance and self-healing. She was inspired to write Lifting Your Spirits because of the benefits she derived and the lack of any guide of this kind for people who have been diagnosed with serious illness. She draws on the insights of friends who shared their own stories of coping with illness, and of healthcare colleagues and practitioners who supported her on her journey.

Edited by: Dr Craig Brown

Contributors from The Janki Foundation for Global Health Care:

Dr Craig Brown   Dr Kala Mistry
Arnold Desser   Bhavna Patani
Dr Sarah Eagger   Joy Rendell

CD credits: See back cover flap

Acknowledgements

The seven tools were first developed by a Janki Foundation healthcare group, including the author, as the basis for a personal and team development programme for healthcare professionals called *Values in Healthcare: a spiritual approach* (The Janki Foundation for Global Health Care, 2004 www.jankifoundation.org).

With sincere thanks to the following for their additional contributions to the booklet and CDs:

Susan Balmforth, Lou Beckerman, Michal Curry, Dr David Goodman, Suman Kalra, Margaret McCathie, Michelle Melon, Maggie Parle, Jana Stanfield, Matthew Stephenson, Chris Wilson, Simon Wong and Dr Harvey Zarren

and to all those who have given feedback, advice and support, including Margaret Barron, Maureen Goodman, Neville Hodgkinson, Himanshu Panchal, Jaymini Patel and Ruth Sewell.

With special thanks from the author to the following for their healing and guiding wisdom: Lou Beckerman, Rex Brangwyn, Dr Craig Brown, Peter Dale, Dr Neil Hodson, Dottie Hook, Sister Jayanti, Derin Waller, Chris Wilson, Dr Harvey Zarren and my children, Dan, Steph and Charly.

Endorsements

reMEmber (www.remembercfs.org.uk) is a charity which helps people with ME (myalgic encephalomyelitis) - also known as CFS (chronic fatigue syndrome) - get the best possible treatment and advice to enable them to lead happy and healthy lives.

"An excellent guide, in a simple format, to help ME patients to treat themselves with compassion and dignity, and also to address their physical, emotional and spiritual needs. LYS sits comfortably with pacing - the tried and tested method of managing the illness."
Janice Kent, Director of reMEmber

The Haven (www.thehavencentre.com) is an information and support centre offering free services for people, their families and carers coping with life limiting illnesses.

"Lifting Your Spirits has proved inspirational to me, encouraging me to pilot a relaxation course for our clients based on the pack. The CD is of a very good quality and has a good mixture of music and voices."
Elizabeth Kelly, Complementary therapist, The Haven Blantyre Health Centre, Scotland

Portsmouth City Primary Care Trust, Older Persons Mental Health service - a day hospital setting.

"Lifting Your Spirits has been successfully used in a day hospital setting in a weekly group for older people with anxiety and depression. It is being recommended across the primary care trust for use by staff and patients alike."
Kate Legg, Occupational Therapy Team Leader, Older Persons Mental Health, Portsmouth City Primary Care Trust

New Approaches to Cancer (www.anac.org.uk) is a national registered charity that offers practical and financial help in all areas of complementary therapy for people affected by cancer.

The British Holistic Medical Association (www.bhma.org) is an open association of mainstream healthcare professionals, CAM practitioners, and members of the public who want to adopt a more holistic approach in their own life and work.

Help the Hospices (www.helpthehospices.org.uk) is a national charity supporting hospice care throughout the UK, providing information and support to patients, carers and all those interested in hospice and palliative care.

"With financial support from various charitable trusts, I have been able to give copies of Lifting Your Spirits to hospices, voluntary organisations and individuals. For example, a hospital in Motherwell is using it with elderly mental health patients which is proving very helpful and a stress centre in Glasgow lends the packs out to the users to help them with their stress."
Margaret McCathie, Laughter therapist, Stirling, Scotland

Users' Feedback

"I thought that the people quoted were describing how I felt when diagnosed with MS... here was someone who really knew what it was like, someone who was speaking from the heart directly to me."

"I loved the description of the woman laughing with her daughter when she jumped out from behind the washing line. People forget that you can still laugh when you are ill."

"The idea of smiling down to my heart, lungs and internal organs made me feel wonderful."

"My favourite track is Flawless diamond - truly inspiring and uplifting."

"The tracks made me realise how much tension I had and that it was okay for me to stop doing and find peace."

"I think the overall voice of the author is authentic, empathetic and true"

Experiences from various clients at The Haven, Blantyre Health Centre, Scotland

*"I gave **Lifting Your Spirits** to two of my friends, both of whom found them really, really helpful... the best help they have received."*

Rosemary Stratton, Eastbourne

"I gave my copy to a young mother of three who was awaiting a bone marrow transplant. Thank you for providing a tool that is sensitive and positive in trying times."

Marion Graham, Development Coach, Soul Success Ltd, Scotland

*"Andy (who has had a stroke) really likes **Lifting Your Spirits**... our plan is to do it as a kind of programme and work through all the seven tools."*

Carol and Andy Mealing, Brighton, East Sussex

"I gave my aunt (who has cancer) a copy. She said, 'I love it. As soon as I get back from chemotherapy I lie down and play it to help me recover."

A client with depression said, 'It is so relaxing. It takes me out of my stressed and anxious feelings and allows me to feel calm and peaceful.'"

Sue Bayliss, Director, Sulis Consulting, Norwich

Introduction

This guide has been developed to offer practical tools for self-help during times of illness. The contents are based on the experiences and insights of people who have coped with serious illness and treatments, with contributions from a range of healthcare practitioners.

When serious illness or disability occurs in our life, it may seem as if we have no control over what is happening and that our well-being lies in the hands of others. However, within ourselves we have a vast capacity to build our resilience on a physical, emotional, mental and spiritual level.

The seven tools in this guide will help you to support yourself in this way, enhancing your sense of well-being and 'lifting your spirits'. By using the booklet and accompanying audio CDs, you will be able to learn how to access inner resources that can sustain you through difficult and challenging times.

Who this guide is for

This guide has been designed for people coping with illness, disability or injury, including those who are:

- diagnosed with a serious physical illness
- coping with pain or disability
- undergoing difficult treatments
- receiving palliative care
- recovering from accident or physical trauma
- experiencing or recovering from mental health problems such as anxiety and depression.

The materials can also benefit hard-pressed carers and healthcare practitioners by introducing ways of nurturing themselves.

Illness and change

The shock of experiencing injury or of being diagnosed with a serious or incurable illness causes major disturbance within all levels of our well-being – physical, mental, emotional and spiritual – as well as in our relationships with family and friends, at work and in other spheres of living. The familiar roles and possessions we thought defined us lose their certainty and we find ourselves confronted with big, unanswerable questions – 'Why this? Why me? Why now?'

Serious illness or injury casts us into a new and unfamiliar role – that of being a 'patient' – and we begin to feel separate and isolated from the seeming normality of life going on around us. We enter a world of waiting – waiting for appointments, for tests, for results, for procedures – where we begin to feel that our health and our future are out of our own control.

Along with this change in our day-to-day life can come a profound sense of loss and a rollercoaster of associated emotions. We may deny or resist the reality of our situation, with feelings of 'this can't be happening to me', 'this shouldn't happen to me' and so on. This kind of reaction breeds disappointment, resentment and frustration. Sometimes we feel that there is no point in life any more and that we may as well give up at the first hurdle. Sometimes we get angry and want to blame someone or something for what is happening. We also talk about 'battling' cancer or 'fighting' depression. While anger may raise our energy to tackle certain problems in the short term, eventually this 'state of war' affects our bodies and minds in ways that drain our energy and increase mental stress, just at a time when we need to marshal our strengths and resources.

As we begin to accept and cope with our illness or disability, we may find ourselves still dwelling on negative thoughts or even picking them up from those around us. These fuel our sense of separateness and can even lead to physical problems, adversely affecting our energy, immune system, digestion, blood pressure etc. Negative thoughts can also create feelings of fatigue, hopelessness, depression and an inability to think clearly or make decisions.

All around us, our partners, close friends and family members will be deeply affected by what is happening. While we want to help them to deal with their own reactions and feelings, we may not have the personal resources to do so.

So how can we keep unnecessary suffering at bay? How can we keep our spirits lifted, and even appreciate the journey illness takes us on?

Illness and opportunity

Many people who have experienced serious illness or disability comment on how it has offered some unforeseen and positive benefits in their lives. These commonly include opportunities for them to:

- slow down and enjoy a gentler pace of life
- reflect on their life situation and make positive changes to their priorities
- observe and take enjoyment from their natural surroundings
- develop more meaningful relationships with partners, friends, family and colleagues
- take up or return to creative pursuits and hobbies
- learn new skills
- deepen their spiritual awareness and practice
- prepare for the future and put their affairs in order.

Surprisingly, illness presents us with unexpected moments of fun, happiness, peace and fulfilment, which arise from a growing ability to live in the moment. We discover personal strengths and qualities we didn't know we had. These help us to cope in positive ways with the change and challenges we face, and to find a new sense of balance and well-being.

Seven helpful tools

The purpose of this guide is to help you to discover and enhance this more positive and gentle way of coping with illness, by practising seven helpful tools in your day-to-day life. In particular, these tools will help you to find and draw upon a quiet place of strength and sustenance inside yourself. While you may be dealing with pain, uncertainty and the distress of others, tapping into this inner sense of resilience will give you a more balanced perspective on what is happening. You can then think and act in ways that are most beneficial for your well-being – physically, mentally, emotionally and spiritually.

The seven tools are:

Tool 1: Meditation
Tool 2: Visualisation
Tool 3: Appreciation
Tool 4: Creativity
Tool 5: Listening
Tool 6: Play
Tool 7: Reflection.

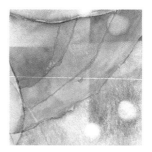

They are all simple practices that you can incorporate into your daily life and healthcare, often for as little as a minute or two. The particular benefits of regular practice may include:

- a lessening of pain, anxiety and distress
- a growing sense of inner peace and stability
- an increase in positive and resourceful thinking and behaviour (which may then have positive effects on others around you)
- greater resilience in your body, mind and emotions
- learning more about who you are and recognising your inner resources
- being able to stand back from difficult situations (which can help you cope more effectively)
- increased fulfilment in relationships with others
- living positively in the present moment and accepting your situation.

Using the tools may also foster or deepen a spiritual connection (for example, to nature or to the Divine) which can support you through difficult stages of your illness, treatment or rehabilitation, as well as give a special meaning to your life.

How to use this guide

The guide consists of a booklet and two audio CDs.

The booklet

Each differently coloured section explores one of the seven tools, and contains:

- a short introduction to the tool and the benefits of using it
- reflections from people who have practised using the tool during times of illness
- some practice ideas for using the tool during your day and in difficult situations relating to your disability, illness or treatment
- reference to one or more tracks on the audio CDs that you can use to deepen your learning and practice
- some positive thoughts you can use on a daily basis.

The audio CDs

The two CDs contain simple, guided visualisations and stories that you can use to relax, prepare for difficult situations and deepen your experience of the power of each tool. You can play these at any time (except while driving or operating machinery) and in any position (seated or lying). Use pillows or cushions to support your body in a restful position. Make sure you are completely comfortable and able to relax deeply for some time without interruption. (The approximate length of each track is given next to its title.)

Some tracks may be particularly helpful before, during and after medical treatments, surgery or therapies, and these are signposted as such.

Most of the tracks are designed to be deeply relaxing, and regular listening will help you to benefit in many ways. Don't worry if you drift off to sleep while listening to a track. You probably needed the extra rest. In time, you may find that you can focus on the content all the way through.

Some of the visualisations are set in particular surroundings, for example, a garden or wood. You may wish to experiment with substituting a comfortable, uplifting setting of your choice as you listen to the track.

We have incorporated a variety of audio experiences onto the CDs, including meditation, visualisation, poetry, stories and song. You may wish to seek out further CDs or tapes of the kind you most enjoy from your local library, bookshops or friends.

Practising

Choose a tool that feels right for you at the time. You can practise them in any order and can decide to use one or two you find particularly helpful, or all seven of them. Read the information in the relevant section of the booklet (or ask someone to read it aloud to you) and then listen to any CD tracks that are signposted.

Try out some of the additional ideas for practice from the booklet over the coming days. If you do not have the energy or motivation to do this, don't judge yourself critically. Just do what you can and feel the benefits. Even if you only relax to a CD track occasionally, it will help to bring about positive change.

At the end of each section of the booklet, you will find some positive thoughts. You can use these in several ways:

- as the basis for a meditation, helping you to bring positive thoughts into your mind
- by saying them to yourself, silently or aloud, at regular intervals during the day or when in a difficult situation
- writing them out and sticking them to your fridge door or somewhere else you will see them regularly during the day.

You might like to make a note of what you do and any changes you notice in your overall sense of well-being or in specific thoughts, feelings and behaviours (see **Tool 7: Reflection**). Above all, show appreciation to yourself for taking some positive steps towards enhancing your well-being.

Relaxation

Before you begin to explore the tools, it may be helpful to learn a method of deep relaxation that you can use on a daily basis or whenever you feel the need, for example, when you feel tired or before going into a difficult situation. We have included two simple relaxation exercises on the CDs, the first based on muscle relaxation and the second focusing on the breath:

 Track 1.1: Going into relaxation (9¹/₂ mins)

Track 1.2: Relaxing breath (4¹/₂ mins)

For a longer, deeper relaxation, try the following track:

 Track 1.8: Healing mist (9 mins)

A note about the word 'healing'

Throughout this guide, we use the word 'healing' to describe some of the tools and their benefits. It is important to distinguish between 'healing' and 'cure' or 'curing', particularly in the context of illness, since they have very different meanings. When we use 'healing', we mean a process or activity that has a positive effect on our sense of well-being. This may be something that helps us to 'feel better' in a physical sense, but it can also refer to improving our mental, emotional or spiritual well-being. Healing can boost our overall resilience, which can help enormously in how we respond to and recover from illness. Even when a condition is untreatable or terminal, it is possible to benefit greatly from the healing effects of the tools in this guide. However, this is not the same as being 'cured', i.e. 'made better' from a physical or mental condition.

A note about the word 'spiritual'

Sometimes we refer to benefits of using the seven tools that may be enjoyed on a 'spiritual' level. Our definition of 'spirituality' is 'looking inwards to discover our true identity'. Using the tools in this guide can help you to explore your innermost qualities and what gives meaning and purpose to your life. Spirituality is a journey of self-discovery that does not only lead inward but, ultimately, also leads outward. In this sense, you may also find that you gain a sense of connection with 'something' or 'some being' greater than yourself. For some, this connection is expressed through the practice of a religion. For others, it is a deep sense of being in touch with nature, a universal consciousness or something divine.

Meditation: discovering the power of peace

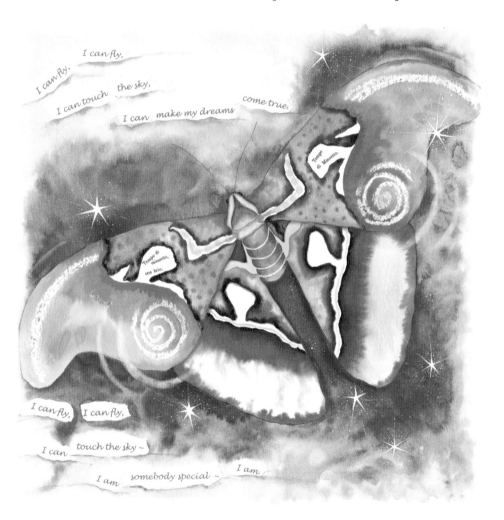

6 When I find my inner peace
I can handle anything. 9

Meditation

Finding a time for silence gives us an opportunity to discover our inner peace. It enhances our general health and well-being, and instils a sense of stability during the turbulence of illness or trauma. The practice of quietening and focusing the mind is often called meditation and there are many meditation techniques. Many people say that they cannot meditate because they are unable to 'still' the mind. Instead of trying to stop thinking, we can just focus on peaceful thoughts. Even a minute spent in this way takes our minds off pain and worries and leaves us feeling refreshed. It helps us to surface some inner qualities such as love or patience, which can strengthen and nurture us on every level.

As you practise bringing peaceful thoughts and images into your mind, it is very common for unwanted thoughts to pop up. Treat your mind as you would a small child who is distracted or misbehaving. Keep guiding it gently back to your desired focus, again and again. In time, you will find that you can experience brief moments of stillness and silence between your thoughts. This is the essence of meditation.

Benefits during illness

Using meditation:

- reduces anxiety, fear and stress
- reduces our experience of pain
- improves sleep
- increases positive thoughts and psychological strength
- helps us to develop self-knowledge and self-reliance
- promotes feelings of peacefulness and spiritual connection.

Reflections

Following my diagnosis, I found it difficult to sit in silence. My mind teemed with anxious thoughts and was continually drawn to what was going on in my body, in particular to the pain experienced from a fast-growing tumour. However, there were fleeting moments in which I could just observe my pain, as if I were detached from my physical body. It was in these moments that I began to experience a brief sense of peace.

When I capture a feeling of peace, the pain and fear seem to diminish. I notice a settling in myself and the confusion. I can begin to look in a detached way at the implications and the challenges of my illness and treatment. As I begin to feel calmer, negative thoughts and emotions occur less frequently. Sometimes I even feel great waves of happiness and a sense of connection with everything.

Since I began to recover from severe depression, I started my own meditation practice. I imagine being on a beach beside an ocean of peace. With each breath I absorb peace into every cell of my body. It leaves me refreshed and feeling that I have something to give to myself and others. Meditating on peace in this way has helped me to discover that even when you have something uncomfortable in your mind, it doesn't mean that you don't have peace and love deep within your heart.

Practising

* Stop for a minute at intervals during the day and let peaceful thoughts enter your mind. Use some of the positive thoughts at the end of this section to help you.

* Find opportunities for developing a sense of peace, for example, by watching a starry sky, stroking a pet, or listening to gentle music or sounds of nature.

* Listen to the following CD tracks for some short meditations on peace and healing that you can do either seated or lying down:

   Track 1.3: Practising peace through becoming silent (5 mins)

  Track 1.4: A peaceful anchor (6 mins)

  Track 1.5: Healing meditation (9 mins)

* Practise feeling peaceful before you go into any difficult situation, or when you are feeling fear or anxiety. (You can use **Track 1.4: A peaceful anchor** to help you.)

A walking values meditation

Sometimes it is difficult to sit still, especially when we are in pain or distracted by what is happening in our bodies or minds. It is still possible to meditate when going about everyday tasks or when moving around. This is a walking meditation, which is linked to some of the positive core beliefs or values we all share:

> Walk at a slow, comfortable pace, preferably on grass or a natural pathway so that you can feel the earth directly under your feet. Allow your breathing to settle into a regular pattern. Look around you and take in the sights, then let your gaze settle gently on a point ahead. Listen to the sounds around you, then let them recede into the background. Feel the air touching your body, the earth under your feet and then let these sensations go.

> As you walk slowly on, let a value like peace come into your mind. Feel it filling your body. Send it out through your feet into the earth and out through your eyes into the world. Say to yourself, 'I am peace'.

> Let another value come into your mind, perhaps love or determination. Again, feel it filling your body. Send it out through your feet into the earth and out through your eyes into the world. Say to yourself 'I am (that value)'.

> Continue in this way, allowing more values to surface in your mind and using them as the basis for your walking meditation. Don't worry if you forget the instructions. Just bring each value into your mind, and feel it 'fill you up' and radiate out from you.

Positive thoughts

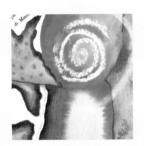

I am a peaceful being.

Finding time for silence gives me an opportunity to discover my inner peace.

I can experience deep peace within.

I stay peaceful and positive in difficult situations.

Through silence I am connected to light, joy and strength.

Visualisation: picturing good health

6 *I like to picture myself full of happiness, good health and energy.* **9**

Visualisation

When we are facing the challenge of illness, treatment or recovery, what we 'see' in our minds can help or hinder us on our journey. Sometimes we conjure up negative scenes that impair our self-confidence and capacity to cope, just at a time when we need to feel strong and good about ourselves. These pictures may be prompted by our own fears and feelings, or by unhelpful things that other people say or do. On the other hand, we can picture positive outcomes, such as our body getting stronger, our mind calming or our spirit growing more peaceful. The tool that can help us to do this is known as visualisation.

Visualisation is not just about seeing pictures in our heads. It is about using all our senses to create a positive vision of how we would like things to be. Depending on which senses are easiest for us to tap into, we can see, touch, hear and smell scenes that are helpful to our sense of well-being. Along with these, we can use positive words to create uplifting thoughts and feelings. Imagining ourselves coping, and feeling safe and well, can help us to overcome difficulties and counter our own and others' negative thoughts, words and actions.

Benefits during illness

Using visualisation:

- improves our ability to relax
- creates positive thoughts, images and feelings
- boosts our resilience and natural immunity
- increases our capacity to cope
- helps us to feel safe and in control.

Reflections

Many people, including healthcare practitioners, used negative words to describe my cancer treatments and possible side-effects – for example, 'toxic' and 'burning'. I decided to visualise the treatments as being gentle and healing. I sensed each beam of radiotherapy as a shaft of sunshine, penetrating my body in a kindly way. I felt my skin as cool and intact, without inflammation. I saw the chemotherapy as a beautiful, golden liquid supporting my body to heal itself and dissolving cells which were not helpful to my well-being. I imagined my vein opening in acceptance to it, without difficulty or irritation. I practised seeing myself undergoing my treatments in a calm and lighthearted way, with all the supports I needed around me.

When I start getting really anxious about going into a situation, it's hard not to see myself panicking or running away. So now, as soon as this kind of image creeps into my mind, I make it shrink in size. I see it flying into a little black box in a corner of a room far away from me. In its place, I put a big, bright, happy picture of myself in the situation. I see and feel myself staying calm, smiling and doing whatever I need to do very competently. If a negative thought comes, I get the positive picture back again as quickly as I can and breathe deeply as I watch myself succeeding. As I practise this more and more, I am finding that I can go into difficult situations and do it for real. I'm proud of my achievement.

Facing major surgery initiated many negative feelings. How could I overcome the intense fear that seemed to be controlling my thoughts and dragging me into a very dark place? I decided to try using visualisation. I knew that for visualisation to work well I needed to use all five senses – seeing, hearing, touching, tasting, smelling – and practise as many times as possible throughout the days prior to the event. I pictured a large TV screen and watched an imaginary film of myself going through the entire process – leaving home, so relaxed, arriving at the hospital, cheerful and at ease, going through all the medical procedures, calm and strong, going down to theatre, peaceful and confident, seeing my surgeon as the best in the world, so I would have a very good outcome and a quick recovery. My surgeon was amazed at how relaxed my body was during the operation and had never experienced a patient recover from this type of surgery so quickly!

Practising

Many people find it difficult to see pictures in their mind. Successful visualisation only requires that you sense or get a feeling of the scene in whatever way is possible for you.

✳ Create a vision in your mind of how you would like to be – for example, a healthy, vibrant and happy person – using some of the positive thoughts at the end of this section. Try to really sense yourself. What do you look like? What colours are you wearing? Where are you? What are you doing? What can you hear yourself saying (or are you singing)? What physical sensations do you have in your body? How does it feel to be you? Add as much detail to your image as you can. Practise visualising yourself in this way as soon as you wake in the morning, during difficult times during the day, and last thing at night before you sleep.

✳ Visualisation can be helpful to practise before going into challenging situations. Take time to relax and then visualise yourself in the situation in as much detail as you can, several times a day. Focus on your strengths, see yourself coping well and notice that you have all the supports around you that you need. You will begin to find that you can capture the positive energy this practice provides the minute you need it.

✳ Before practising visualisation, you will need to be relaxed. Listen to the following relaxation CD tracks to help you prepare:

Track 1.1: Going into relaxation (9½ mins)

Track 1.2: Relaxing breath (4½ mins)

✳ Listen to the following CD tracks for some guided, healing visualisations that you can do either seated or lying down:

Track 1.6: Being cared for (4 mins)

Track 1.7: Inner sanctuary (6 mins)

Track 1.8: Healing mist (9 mins)

✳ If you are preparing for surgery or medical treatment, you may like to use the following, longer CD track:

 Track 1.9: Bluebell wood (21 mins)

This visualisation can be practised before, during and after surgery, treatments or therapies. It is set in a bluebell wood as nature has its own healing power. However, you can visualise an alternative setting if you wish, such as a mountain, meadow or garden.

Positive thoughts

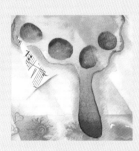

I experience well-being with all my senses.

I see myself being calm and confident as I go through the day.

All the organs in my body are healthy and strong. All the cells in my body vibrate with radiant good health.

I picture myself making confident decisions for my own wellness.

I belong to all creation and I am always good enough.

Appreciation: giving thanks

I feel grateful for just being here today.

Appreciation

While feelings like anger, jealousy and simmering resentment can feed illness, feeling positive aids recovery and boosts the immune system. One of the most effective ways of lifting ourselves out of negative thinking is to actively appreciate the good in ourselves and our lives.

It might seem odd to focus on being appreciative in situations that involve difficult treatments and uncertain outcomes. However, showing appreciation on a regular basis can make you feel better in both body and mind. The tool of appreciation honours those things in life that give us health, vitality and success.

Appreciation is really about noticing and affirming the good about ourselves, about others and about the world around us. Beginning with ourselves, we can think about all the unique qualities we have and all the things we are able to do, however small. We can also remember all the positive things we have in our lives and all those fulfilling experiences we have had.

Next, we can extend this practice to others, by noticing their 'goodness', rather than finding fault and opportunities for criticism. When we show appreciation to others, it is helpful to be very specific. For example, we can say what it was about what they did that we found helpful. It is also important to show sincerity in the way that we voice our appreciation, for example, in tone of voice and gesture. When hard-pressed carers, whether healthcare professionals, volunteers or family, receive unexpected thanks and positive feedback in this way, they will feel 'topped up' and better able to continue with their efforts to care for and support us.

We can also give thanks for our surroundings. We can relish the comfort of a warm bed or a relaxing bath. We can appreciate the beauty of nature through a window or when we are outdoors.

Showing appreciation can be a stepping-stone to the expression of deep gratitude. Even the most challenging days bring gifts to be grateful for, and feeling and showing gratitude becomes like a plate of tasty food, nourishing us from within. It can also become the basis for spiritual practice, when we give thanks to the Divine or to a greater power for guiding and sustaining us.

Benefits during illness

Using appreciation:

- enhances our health and our immune system
- boosts positive thinking, motivation and self-esteem
- provides positive feedback and reinforcement for others
- creates an atmosphere of mutual respect and good feelings
- provides a basis for spiritual connection.

Reflections

I remember to show appreciation to myself. As I wake each morning, I smile into each part of my body, each organ, my bones and muscles, my blood and every healthy cell in my body, thanking them for coping with the treatments and helping me to heal. I thank myself for staying calm in a difficult situation, carrying out a simple task or managing to go for a walk.

After a particularly difficult examination, I gave some specific thanks to the nurse by saying, "Thank you for holding my hand in such a caring way during the examination. It really helped me to stay calm." Remembering to show appreciation gives me some control over what is happening to me. It encourages me to think positively in the most difficult situations. I then tend to act positively and my actions affect others around me in positive ways. It's like a virtuous circle.

I decided to look at my treatment, while difficult, as something to be grateful for. As I swallowed each tablet I visualised it healing my body. I showed gratitude to the staff who attended me and gave my sincere thanks to friends who supported me. I gave a box of chocolates to the car park attendant at the cancer centre on my final day of radiotherapy as he had always greeted me with such a cheerful smile.

I had been depressed for years. It felt as though the world was against me; everything I did turned out badly, relationships failed and nothing I did or any medication I took seemed to help. Then one day an old friend, who must have been fed up with my moaning, said to me something quite simple: "How would you like things to be in the future?" At first I was annoyed with her, but later, when I thought about what she said, I started to think about how things could be better. I began to think more positively and to find something to appreciate in each day. I noticed my "luck" changed and I began to feel better. It took some time for me to change my habit of negative thinking. Slowly the depression has lifted and now I'm grateful for the life I have.

Practising

✳ Congratulate yourself for something you have achieved, however small. You might like to give yourself a treat as a reward!

✳ As soon as you wake up each day, think of at least one thing you are grateful for in your life. You may like to jot your thoughts down to remind yourself during the day. Repeat the practice just before you go to sleep.

✳ If you are able, spend some time outside in nature as a powerful way of taking you 'outside yourself'. Appreciate everything you can see, feel and hear. If you are unable to go out, put some natural things around you to look at, hold or smell, for example, a vase of flowers, an attractive pebble or stone, a pine cone.

✳ Give special attention to a pet or grow a plant in a pot and take care of it. Looking after something can help you to feel better.

✳ Practise appreciation at the beginning or end of the day by listening to this CD track:

 Track 2.1: Giving thanks (12¹/₂ mins)

✳ If you are about to go into surgery or treatment of any kind, you may like to practise appreciation by way of preparation, using the following, longer CD track:

 Track 1.9: Bluebell wood (21 mins)

Positive thoughts

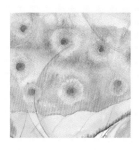

I appreciate who I am and everything I do.

I give thanks to my body for all that it is able to do.

I give thanks to those who care for me.

I appreciate the beauty of my surroundings/my garden/nature.

When I feel tired, I remember happy times and I regain strength.

Creativity: learning to express ourselves

6 *When I am being creative I feel alive and full of energy.* 9

Creativity

Illness can be a time when we are moved to express ourselves through writing, painting or other creative pursuits. We can also discover a capacity to generate creative solutions to problems.

Giving 'voice' to our unique creativity is essentially healing on all levels and has been recognised as such by the introduction of a range of art therapies in healthcare. When we express ourselves creatively, we engage the intuitive, right side of the brain, rather than the left side, which is dominated by logic and reason. Any creative pursuits can help us to bypass our busy, thinking mind and reach a still place from which we can generate new ideas, explore our feelings and connect with ourselves at a deeper level. They can also revitalise our energies and provide a sense of fulfilment.

Many of us say that we are not creative, perhaps remembering the childlike drawings or paintings we produced long ago. Instead, let's think about creativity as a process, one that allows us to explore and learn about ourselves. We can go about our simple, everyday activities in a creative way. Arranging flowers in a vase, food on a plate, hair on a head or words on a page are all examples of ways in which we can express our unique creativity.

We can also spend time in creative pursuits like painting, writing, music, gardening or sewing. In fact, illness can present us with unexpected time and opportunity to take up or return to a creative hobby, perhaps something we always wanted to do. The important thing is to enjoy and immerse ourselves in the doing, rather than be concerned about what we produce at the end.

Learning to relax deeply can be a first step to being creative, as we set aside current concerns and calm the busy mind. Once we are fully engaged in the creative process, we feel free from the constraints of our bodies, our minds and our situation.

Benefits during illness

Using creativity:

- helps us to generate new ideas and solutions to problems
- enables us to access a quality of peacefulness, free from worry and pain
- provides a route to exploring our feelings and learning more about ourselves
- allows us to express ourselves in our own, unique ways.

Reflections

Once involved in the creative process, it is such a relief to stop thinking – about my illness, my discomfort, my treatment, the outcomes, and so on. I start the sculpture class feeling exhausted and uncomfortable. As I work the clay beneath my fingers, I think of nothing. I enter an empty space full of potential where time ceases to exist. Out of this still space I can create something of my true self. I have never done sculpture before and yet the face and head which emerges is almost alive in its real-ness, full of understanding and compassion. As I work, I stroke the contours I create. I hold the face gently in my hands and I come into my original self – a wholly creative being.

I collected together all the beautiful cards that people had sent during my illness. I cut out some of the most inspiring images and words and sat down to make a collage. I got quite carried away with glue and glitter and felt like a child again. While I worked I pictured my own "wellness" and a very beautiful and surprising picture emerged. I put it on the wall and still look at it every day when I'm feeling tired or down.

Practising

∗ Take up an old hobby or try a creative activity that you have always wanted to do. Start small so that you can work within the limits of your energy and get some instant enjoyment. For example, plant a container, rather than tackle a whole flower bed.

∗ Find or make a small object that provides some inspiration for you, such as a family photo, a religious or spiritual symbol or a piece of embroidery. You might wish to keep this with you when you are resting at home, going into hospital or having treatments.

∗ As a further step, collect other objects that represent healing or inspiration for you and keep them in an attractive box or bag. These might include cards or words of greeting you have been sent from friends or family, a quotation or poem you have enjoyed, a stone, shell, dried flower or piece of fabric with a pleasing colour or texture, and a CD with a story or music that gives you good feelings. You can continue to gather objects as they come into your life. Open the container whenever you need a 'lift' for your spirits.

∗ Listen to the following CD track to appreciate your unique creativity:

 Track 2.2: Relaxing into creativity (6 mins)

Positive thoughts

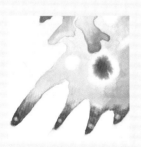

I am a uniquely creative being.

I can express my creativity in many ways.

I can always find time for expressing my creativity without any feelings of guilt.

I know that I can create good solutions to problems by allowing my creativity to flow.

Being creative helps me to come into my true and wonderful self.

Listening: deepening our connection with others

❝ When I listen with my whole self, it feels healing for both me and the other person. ❞

Listening

Really listening to others and encouraging them to listen to us is an important step in promoting the well-being of both ourselves and our carers. A common complaint among patients is that we are not listened to by healthcare professionals. We feel anxious when we come in for a consultation or procedure, and find it difficult to explain our experiences and concerns. We 'hear' what the practitioner is saying, yet remember little of it afterwards. Consultations are time-limited, and healthcare professionals themselves can feel stressed and unsupported. Similar pressures exist for our carers at home. Our family will be worrying about us and we feel anxious for them. No wonder that patients, practitioners and carers are not always in the 'right space' to listen to and connect with each other.

A few minutes of deep and active listening improves communication and the sense of being connected to each other. It helps to create a feeling of mutual satisfaction at home, at the end of a treatment or during a consultation.

Effective listening means concentrating on what the other person is saying, without the interruption of our own thoughts and feelings. The first step is for us to relax into a state of calmness, so that our minds can be clear and receptive. If we are fully present for the other person in this way, then they will be fully present for us and we can both reap the benefits. By listening deeply, we 'model' the qualities we would like to receive from the other person and an atmosphere of tolerance and open-heartedness is created.

If we are talking with a healthcare practitioner about our illness or treatment, we may rightly feel some anxiety. However, if we can trust that it is the other person's intention to help or support us, this will help us to relax and we can then listen with our complete attention.

One note of caution: it is not always realistic to expect medical professionals to listen to our wider anxieties and feelings as well as to manage our healthcare treatment. We may need to seek out a friend, counsellor, specialist nurse or chaplain for our emotional, psychological and spiritual support.

Benefits during illness

Using deep listening:

- helps to neutralise feelings of anxiety and anger
- benefits the listener as well as the receiver
- creates an atmosphere of tolerance and mutual caring.

Reflections

I find it difficult to remember what my doctor says, so I try to take a friend to help me listen. Sometimes I take a tape recorder and ask if it's ok to record the conversation.

I find that when I sit with friends, family or helpers in an open and peaceful way, I am able to listen from the heart, with full interest, rather than my mind running on to what I want to say or interrupting them. This quality of listening generates feelings of love and compassion, which I think is helpful for them as well as for myself.

I experiment with deep listening when I am with my consultant. It seems to remove some of the barriers between "patient" and "doctor". It is as if I am setting an example of how I wish to be treated and this is then responded to. I am able to tell my story in my own way and to have this listened to and understood. This feels good for me and, I think, for him too.

Practising

＊ Practise relaxing before a consultation. This will help you to stay calm throughout the discussion, examination or treatment. You may find the following CD tracks helpful for this:

Track 1.1: Going into relaxation (9¹/₂ mins)

Track 1.2: Relaxing breath (4¹/₂ mins)

* When you first meet a healthcare practitioner, remember to make eye contact, even if you are lying down. Extend a greeting and, if there is the opportunity, ask how they are or show some interest in them as an individual, rather than just as your practitioner.

* Prepare for a good listening experience by doing the following:
  - Make a list of two or three important questions you want answers to, as well as any important information you want to give about your symptoms or progress. Take this list with you to your appointment.
  - Check with the practitioner whether they have enough time to deal with your list of concerns at the beginning of the consultation.
  - If you feel you need it, ask if additional help or information is available for your situation.

* When you are in a discussion with a practitioner, supporter or friend, you can practise deep listening by following these steps:
  - adopt an easy, open posture
  - breathe in a calm and regular way
  - bring peaceful thoughts into your mind
  - imagine that your heart is opening towards the other person
  - be fully attentive and don't let your mind wander or 'switch off'
  - feel respect for the other person's 'story' or point of view
  - stay quiet and refrain from interrupting, making faces or moving while they are speaking.

  Try it out, and make a mental note of how it felt for you and how the person responded to you. When it is your turn to speak, remember to be clear and assertive about what you want to ask or say.

* If you are going to try deep listening during a healthcare consultation, you might like to practise beforehand by visualising yourself going through the above steps in the room (see **Tool 2: Visualisation**). See and feel the positive response you receive from those you are listening to, and then experience yourself being listened to in a positive and healing way.

* You can also use the following CD track to prepare for a consultation:

 Track 2.3: The listening bowl (10 mins)

Positive thoughts

I can listen to others in a peaceful way, even in difficult situations.

When I open my heart, I can listen with full concentration and respect.

When I express my concerns, I am listened to and understood.

I am able to tell my story in my own way.

When I really listen, I can create feelings of trust and friendship.

Play: enjoying the benefits of fun and laughter

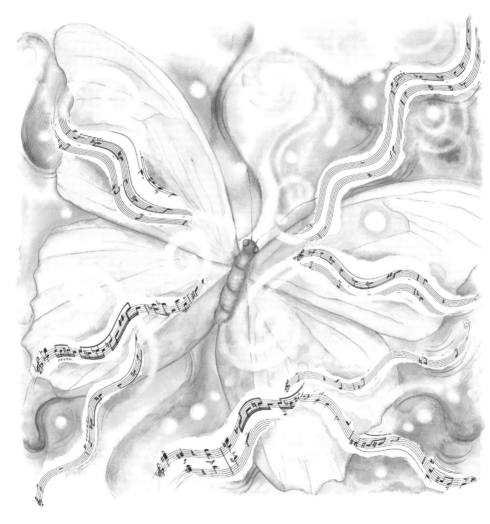

I deserve to have fun and to enjoy life.

Play

Illness is a serious business, and people around us may feel that it is only appropriate to be solemn. Yet being playful and light-hearted lifts our own mood as well as those of our family, friends and carers.

When we watch children play, they seem to be totally caught up in the moment, unaware of how they look to the outside world. In contrast, we usually picture adults playing organised sports or perhaps musical instruments, where there are many rules and norms of behaviour. As adults, we rarely consider playing for playing's sake. In fact, we may feel that it is childish or indulgent to just 'play'. We feel embarrassed at the very thought of making fools of ourselves in front of other people. Yet it is play that allows us to drop the roles and masks we wear and bring more of who we truly are to the fore. It encourages us to be accepting and tolerant of ourselves, our situations and other people.

We can learn to be 'play-full' in the way in which we engage with life, even during times of illness. We all have a playful side and when we find it we experience a wonderful feeling of liberation and 'lightness'. If we let our inner joyful nature shine through, we will reap many healing benefits.

With play, the activity and any goals are unimportant, as long as we are doing something we enjoy. The important thing is to allow ourselves to be spontaneous and carefree, willing to take the risk of getting it wrong. Playing with others, whether through board games, bowling or dancing, has an important social dimension. It encourages a quality of interaction that can be more fulfilling than our normal conversations and contacts.

Laughter, too, is extremely therapeutic. It has proven physical and mental benefits, including boosting the immune system, providing aerobic exercise for the heart and diaphragm, improving sleep, enhancing mental function, increasing pain tolerance and boosting our sense of well-being. Laughter releases endorphins (feel-good hormones) around our bodies. No wonder clowns are now being introduced onto hospital wards.

Laughing with ourselves and others helps us to put things in perspective and learn from our behaviour. It enhances self-esteem and enables us to connect with others at a deeper level.

Benefits during illness

Using play and laughter:

- provides relaxation and reduces stress
- diffuses anger and negative emotions
- helps us to put things in perspective and see the 'lighter' side
- helps us to overcome barriers and difficulties
- provides many health benefits, both physical and mental
- enables self-expression and self-learning
- promotes better communication with others.

Reflections

I hung out some bed sheets in the sunshine and was in deep thought. Suddenly, a large shape loomed at me through the washing and gave me a big fright. The laughing face of my daughter appeared through a gap in the sheets. In that instant, I knew I had two choices. I could cover up my unnecessary fear and embarrassment by being angry with her and critical of her silly behaviour; or, I could laugh at my reactions and join her in her playfulness. I quickly started laughing. We laughed and laughed together and then we hugged for a long time. I knew I had created a healing moment of connection.

Following my accident, I was immobilised for a long time. My young grandson would visit me sometimes after school and bring a variety of board games. I hadn't played any games since I was a kid and yet I found myself totally engrossed. It was me who shouted and laughed loudest when the stakes got high! The time flew and I forgot how frustrated I had been about being stuck in a chair all day.

Practising

- Spend some time each day doing something you enjoy and can play at, such as cooking, playing board games, painting or singing. Let go of any expectations about how well you might perform; just focus on the enjoyment.

- Keep a mental note of each time you have a good laugh or show your playful side. What sparked this moment off? How did you respond? How did you feel? How did others respond?

* Ask your friends to send you jokes or lend you funny films to watch. Even better, ask them to share these funny moments with you.

* Visualise yourself being light-hearted and having fun (see **Tool 2: Visualisation**).

* Smile at yourself in the mirror. Smile at other people and notice their reactions. Smiling, like laughter, is infectious and makes others feel good too. You, in turn, get to reap the benefit of their good feelings!

* When you need some inspiration for having fun, listen to the following CD track. This is an uplifting story about how laughter helped one woman to recover from serious illness and use the benefits of laughter to help many others:

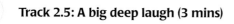 **2.4: The healing power of laughter (4 mins)**

* Try out an exercise in smiling and laughing by listening to the following track:

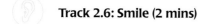 **Track 2.5: A big deep laugh (3 mins)**

* If you need a lift during the day, listen to the poem on the next track:

Track 2.6: Smile (2 mins)

Positive thoughts

I can play and have fun just for the sake of it.

When I allow my playful side to emerge, others join me in my light-heartedness.

Laughing helps me to connect with others and express who I really am.

A sense of humour makes difficult things easy and heavy things light.

When I see life as a game, my lightness of spirit makes problems seem easier.

Reflection: making time for meeting ourselves

I focus on how far I have come, rather than how far I have to go.

Reflection

The experience of illness or trauma often leads us to dwell on the past and how things used to be. This can naturally lead to a sense of loss and feelings of sadness, denial or anger. However, illness also offers a rare opportunity to take a fresh look at what is important and gives meaning in our lives. We can take time for reflection.

Making time for reflection can help us to remember our enduring strengths and qualities, and make sense of illness as part of life's journey. From a place of calm and peacefulness, we can stand back and look at ourselves and what has happened, from the outside. We can begin to understand our own reactions and release any feelings of anger, anxiety and attachment. We can then focus on how far we have come, not how far we have to go. This helps us to build on our positive experiences and strengthen our self-esteem.

Reflection as a tool is about processing our thoughts and experiences from a place of stillness and without judgment. As we practise, we can recognise mistakes we have made without feeling we have failed. If we have feelings of guilt, we can forgive others and forgive ourselves. We begin to take a more detached view about what is happening, and learn from our experiences. We can also focus on the positive contributions we made and what went right in a situation.

Reflection can also help us to come to a place of acceptance concerning our illness and to prepare for the future, whatever it holds, on a practical, emotional or spiritual level.

Benefits during illness

Using reflection:

- enables us to observe and let go of negative emotions
- helps us to learn from our mistakes
- increases acceptance and contentment in our life
- reduces stress
- boosts self-esteem
- helps us to consider the future, whatever it holds.

Reflections

Although I earn my living by writing, I found I was totally unable to write a word for the first year of my illness and treatment. Instead, I drew flowers on a page and coloured them in, one petal, each day at a time, in a colour that caught my mood. Soon I had bunches of brilliant flowers which summarised my journey through courses of chemotherapy and radiotherapy. Through reflection I realised that illness is not a hiatus in life – it is part of living and needs to be lived to the full. It brings many blessings and opportunities for self-learning.

Confined to bed for long periods because of my illness, I began to think of the holidays we took as a family over all those years. I would choose one holiday and try and remember it in as much detail as I could – the weather, the places we visited, the food, and so on. But what came back most was people's friendliness and the fun we had. It made me feel good.

Looking back, I became aware that I had always been hard on my body and mind, pushing them despite their limitations, often in the face of tiredness or sickness. I had indeed battled with my own physical self. I have learned that acceptance of illness is not a state of "giving up", but rather a state of grace which is gentle on the body, mind and spirit and encourages healing at all levels. I have forgiven myself for the past and now spend time nurturing myself without feeling guilty.

Now that my time is limited, reflecting on my own gives me an opportunity to think about dying. I am able to put things in order and give some of my special possessions to friends and family. Talking about my plans and wishes is comforting for me and for the special people in my life.

Practising

* While relaxing, think about good things that have happened to you in your life, for example, a holiday or a personal achievement, and how they felt for you at the time. You may like to look at photograph albums or mementos to help you recall significant events.

* Think about recent events and feelings, perhaps at the end of a day or week. Rather than focusing on failures, make a mental note of what went well for you, what you achieved (however small) and what you have learned about your qualities and strengths. You might ask yourself these questions:
  - What made me feel content today (or this week)?
  - Where was I successful today (or this week)?
  - What have I learned about myself?

* Take a few minutes on a regular basis to sit peacefully and reflect on your life and its meaning, for example, on the importance of family, your work, the opportunities you have.

* Some people like to keep a journal and write down these kinds of reflections. As an alternative to keeping a journal, you may feel inspired to draw or paint your reflections, or to write a poem. For inspiration, listen to the following CD track:

 Track 2.7: Flawless diamond (7 mins)

* Besides reflecting on your own, it is important to have a support network. Ask yourself the question, 'Who do I turn to for support in different situations?' Find a friend, partner or colleague you can share difficult issues and feelings with. Sometimes you need someone outside of the situation, possibly a professional counsellor or therapist. Remember to practise your listening skills, too (see **Tool 5: Listening**).

* Practise asking for help. Sometimes this may seem quite alien, particularly if you have always been the one who supports and helps others. However, asking for help makes another person feel useful while providing you with much needed support.

* Choose some music you enjoy listening to, or a poem that has meaning for you at this time, to help you to reflect. There are some examples on the two CD tracks below.

* Listen to the following CD tracks to prompt your own reflections:

 Track 2.8: Waving (3 mins)

Track 2.9: Little Butterfly (6 mins)

Positive thoughts

Each day brings opportunities for me to learn more about myself.

Remaining open to life helps me to reach my full potential.

I appreciate my successes, and learn from my mistakes.

I can move forward when I forgive myself and let go of my mistakes.

Understanding that life is all about learning, I can accept and come to enjoy whatever I do.

❝ Thinking of myself as a traveller through life, I can feel free from the limits of the past and fully enjoy the present. ❞

Going forwards

We hope you have enjoyed this booklet and the CDs. Even if you have tried just one or two tools or listened to some of the CD tracks, the positive energy they create will go with you into all areas of your life. You may find yourself being able to stand back and notice what is happening around you from a more detached perspective. You will then find it easier to respond in a positive and resourceful way.

As challenging situations come up, you may wish to go back to some of the tools that can help you to prepare for these, such as visualisation (**Tool 2**) and listening (**Tool 5**).

If you have time on your hands, give yourself permission to do something creative (**Tool 4**), to play (**Tool 6**) or to sit and reflect (**Tool 7**), just for the sake of it. If you only have a minute, use it to go into silence and peace (**Tool 1**) or to remember something to be grateful for (**Tool 3**). If you only have a few seconds, a smile or laugh will give you and others a helpful boost (**Tool 6**). Before you realise it, you will have put all seven tools into practice!

We wish you well on your journey.

 Track 2.10: Sunshine Warm Upon Your Face (7 mins)

My reflections

This is your space to jot down any reflections on how far you have come and how the tools have helped you.

About the Janki Foundation

The Janki Foundation for Global Health Care is a UK-based healthcare charity dedicated to positive human development. Drawing on research demonstrating that positive states of mind promote health and healing, it has developed a unique personal and team development programme in support of healthcare professionals, called *Values in Healthcare: a spiritual approach.*

Lifting Your Spirits is a companion guide that has been developed specifically for patients. Together, these materials support a whole-person approach to healthcare, an approach that considers the needs of patients and practitioners at all levels of body, mind and spirit.

For further information about these Janki Foundation initiatives and the training opportunities provided, please contact:

The Janki Foundation for Global Health Care
449-451 High Road
London NW10 2JJ
United Kingdom
T +44 (0)20 8459 1400/9090
F +44 (0)20 8459 9091
E info@jankifoundation.org
W www.jankifoundation.org

References: Jan Alcoe, Lifting Your Spirits: A self-help approach to coping with illness. *Journal of holistic healthcare, Vol 5 May 2008 (under Patient self-healing)*

Lifting Your Spirits Courses, workshop and presentations

The Janki Foundation can provide:

• presentations to healthcare and patient support organizations who are interested in introducing the tools and guide as part of their activities

• tailored, experiential workshops for healthcare practitioners on using the tools to support their patients and enhance their own self-care

• courses and group sessions for people coping with illness or disability and their carers on using the tools to support themselves.